Reach
HIGHER

Practice Book

NATIONAL
GEOGRAPHIC
LEARNING

Australia · Brazil · Mexico · Singapore · United Kingdom · United States

National Geographic Learning,
a Cengage Company

Reach Higher Practice Book 3B

Publisher, Content-based English: Erik Gundersen

Associate Director, R&D: Barnaby Pelter

Senior Development Editors:
 Jacqueline Eu
 Ranjini Fonseka
 Kelsey Zhang

Development Editor: Rayne Ngoi

Director of Global Marketing: Ian Martin

Heads of Regional Marketing:
 Charlotte Ellis (Europe, Middle East and Africa)
 Kiel Hamm (Asia)
 Irina Pereyra (Latin America)

Product Marketing Manager: David Spain

Senior Production Controller: Tan Jin Hock

Senior Media Researcher (Covers): Leila Hishmeh

Senior Designer: Lisa Trager

Director, Operations: Jason Seigel

Operations Support:
 Rebecca Barbush
 Drew Robertson
 Caroline Stephenson
 Nicholas Yeaton

Manufacturing Planner: Mary Beth Hennebury

Publishing Consultancy and Composition:
 MPS North America LLC

© 2020 Cengage Learning, Inc.

ALL RIGHTS RESERVED. No part of this work covered by the copyright herein may be reproduced or distributed in any form or by any means, except as permitted by U.S. copyright law, without the prior written permission of the copyright owner.

"National Geographic", "National Geographic Society" and the Yellow Border Design are registered trademarks of the National Geographic Society ® Marcas Registradas

For permission to use material from this text or product,
submit all requests online at **cengage.com/permissions**
Further permissions questions can be emailed to
permissionrequest@cengage.com

ISBN-13: 978-0-357-36690-5

National Geographic Learning
200 Pier Four Blvd
Boston, MA 02210
USA

Locate your local office at **international.cengage.com/region**

Visit National Geographic Learning online at **ELTNGL.com**
Visit our corporate website at **www.cengage.com**

Printed in the United States of America
Print Number: 12   Print Year: 2024

Contents

Unit 5: Mysteries of Matter

Unit 6: From Past to Present

Unit 7: Blast! Crash! Splash!

Unit 8: Getting There

Name _____   Date _____

Mysteries of Matter

Make a concept map with the answers to the Big Question:
What causes matter to change?

What causes matter to change?

© Cengage Learning, Inc.

Thinking Map

Partner Skit

Plan and act out a short skit with a partner. Then use the characters' words to create a character-plot chart about your skit.

Character	What the character says	What this shows about the character	What this shows about the plot

© Cengage Learning, Inc.

Take turns telling your partner about one of the characters. What do the character's words show about the character?

Grammar

What's It Like?

Grammar Rules Adjectives

An **adjective** describes a noun.

An **adjective** can describe how something looks, smells, tastes, feels, or sounds.

An **adjective** can also tell how many or what things are made of.

An **adjective** usually comes before the noun it describes.

Write the best adjective in each blank. Use each adjective only once.

| tiny | three | wet | strawberry | warm | bright |

1. The _____ sunshine wakes me up.

2. The _____ snow begins to melt.

3. The _____ grass starts to grow.

4. I pour _____ jam on _____ pancakes.

5. I am ready for a _____ day.

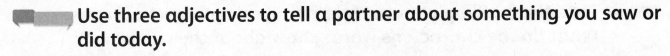 **Use three adjectives to tell a partner about something you saw or did today.**

© Cengage Learning, Inc.

Fluency

"Melt the Snow!"

Use this passage to practice reading with proper expression.

Little Ant [*pointing*]: Look Mommy,	5
the sun is shining. It's melting the snow.	13
It's been such a long winter, and I'm tired of	23
staying indoors. May I go out and play?	31

From "Melt the Snow!" page 14

Expression

B ☐ Does not read with feeling.   A ☐ Reads with appropriate feeling for most content.

I ☐ Reads with some feeling, but does not match content.   AH ☐ Reads with appropriate feeling for all content.

Accuracy and Rate Formula

Use the formula to measure a reader's accuracy and rate while reading aloud.

$$\underline{\hspace{3cm}} - \underline{\hspace{3cm}} = \underline{\hspace{3cm}}$$

words attempted   number of errors   words correct per minute
in one minute   (wcpm)

© Cengage Learning, Inc.

Name _____ Date _____

"Saved in Ice"

Complete the fact cards as you read "Saved in Ice."

- -

That's Amazing!

An amazing fact about _____

is _____

_____

I found it in the article _____

by _____

_____   _____

Name   Date

- -

That's Amazing!

An amazing fact about _____

is _____

_____

I found it in the article _____

by _____

_____   _____

Name   Date

© Cengage Learning, Inc.

Name _____   Date _____

Compare Media

Use the comparison chart to compare an e-mail and a web-based article.

	Rudy's e-mail	"Saved in Ice"
electronic communication	yes	yes
formal language		
informal language		
personal information		
factual information		

 Talk with a partner. Tell whether you liked the article and why or why not.

© Cengage Learning, Inc.

Grammar

The Storm

Grammar Rules Adjectives and Articles

Some adjectives use **demonstrative pronouns** like **this** or **that** to tell "which one."

Examples: **This** *day is warm. Was it warm* **that** *day?*

These *clouds are big. Were* **those** *clouds bigger?*

Articles identify **nouns**.

Examples: **An animal** *died in Russia.*

The mammoth *was about as big as* **a dog**.

Write an article or a demonstrative pronoun in each blank. Then circle the adjectives.

_____ big storm is starting today. _____ storm reminds me of one last year. In _____ storm _____ inch of rain fell every hour. Then _____ rain turned into snow. Strong winds knocked down _____ tree, too. I hope today's storm is smaller. I hope _____ winds are softer. I like _____ tree I can see here. I want to climb _____ tree after the storm.

Use three adjectives and articles to tell a partner a weather story.

© Cengage Learning, Inc.

Thinking Map

Why Did It Happen?

Make a cause-and-effect chart about an event that happened. It could be something that happened to you, or something you read or heard about.

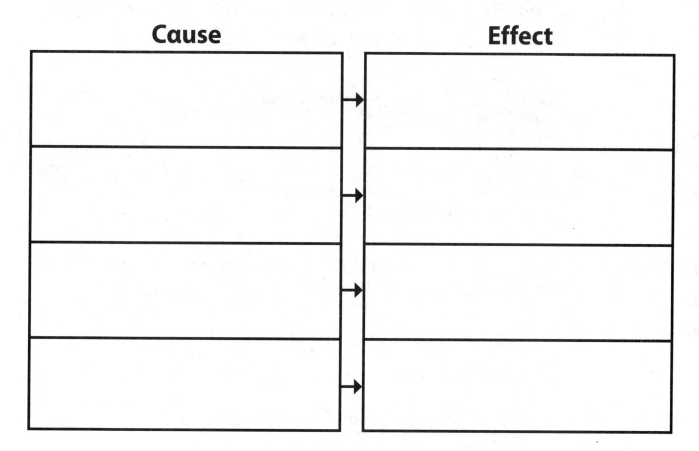

Cause	Effect

 Talk with a partner about the event in your chart. Tell what happened to cause another event to happen. Then do the same with your partner's chart.

© Cengage Learning, Inc.

A Day at the Pond

Grammar Rules Possessive Adjectives

A **possessive adjective** tells who or what owns, has, or is part of something. Put the possessive adjective before the noun.

One	More than one
my	our
your	your
his, her, its	their

Read the first sentence in each pair. Then write a possessive adjective in the second sentence so that it has the same meaning as the first.

1. Today, I walk to the beach with <u>the friends that I have</u>.

   Today, I walk to the beach with _____ friends.

2. "Wear <u>the mittens that you own</u>," said Ana.

   "Wear _____ mittens," said Ana.

3. There is hot chocolate in <u>the backpack that we have</u>.

   There is hot chocolate in _____ backpack.

4. They were glad they wore <u>the boots they own</u>.

   They were glad they wore _____ boots.

 Use two possessive adjectives from the chart. Tell a partner about something you and a friend own, have, or are part of.

© Cengage Learning, Inc.

Name _____   Date _____

"Quicksand: When Earth Turns to Liquid"

Listen as your teacher reads. Follow with your finger.

1

Some people are afraid of quicksand. Movies show people drowning in it. You can find quicksand in places where there is a lot of water. Quicksand is not really dangerous. It is just sand and water. There is so much water in the sand that it cannot hold anything up.

2

Most of the time, the ground is strong. It can hold a person, a car, or a building.

When there is too much water, it pushes the very small sand or dirt pieces away from each other. Then the ground is not strong anymore.

3

Some people believe scary things about quicksand. They think it is alive or that worms that suck blood are in it. These things are not true. Next time you see quicksand in a movie, don't be scared!

© Cengage Learning, Inc.

Grammar

The Possessives Game

Grammar Rules Possessive Nouns

A **possessive noun** tells who or what owns or has something.

For a **singular noun**, add **'s**: *the cat's tail, Rita's books, a dog's paw*

For a **plural noun**, add **s'**: *kids' sneakers, cars' lights, lions' roars*

1. **Play with a partner.**

2. **Cut out the cards. Turn the cards face down.**

3. **Choose one bigger card and one smaller card. If they form the correct possessive noun, keep them. If not, put them face down again. The first player with five correct possessive nouns wins.**

one lion __ teeth	the sand __ temperature	two bear __ claws	a fish __ scales
a few bird __ feathers	five team __ uniforms	ten duck __ quacks	a camel __ hump
ten flower __ seeds	the water __ weight	a school __ students	a room __ shape

's	's	s'	's
s'	s'	s'	's
s'	's	's	's

© Cengage Learning, Inc.

Reread and Retell

"Quicksand: When Earth Turns to Liquid"

Make a cause-and-effect chart for "Quicksand: When Earth Turns to Liquid."

Cause	Effect
Water sinks into the sand..	

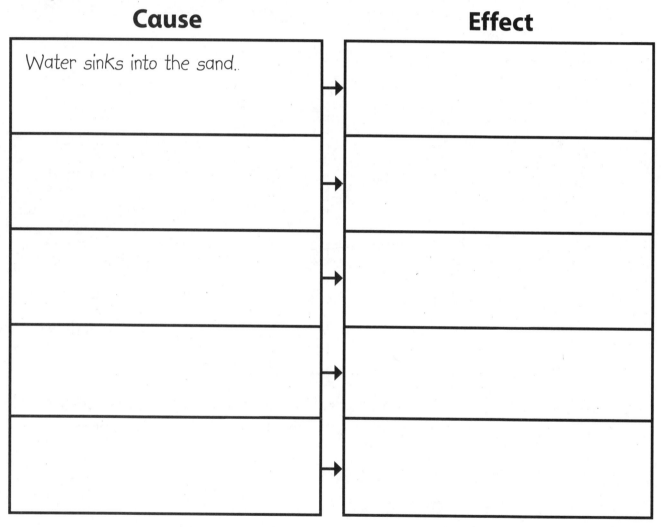

 Use your cause-and-effect chart to summarize the science article for a partner.

© Cengage Learning, Inc.

Phonics Practice

Prefixes: *im-*, *in-*

<u>im</u>possible

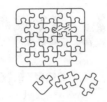
<u>in</u>complete

Read each word. Circle the word that names the picture.

1.		impossible inactive incomplete	**2.** 1 + 1 = 3 incorrect indirect impolite
3.		impolite indirect imperfect	**4.** inactive indirect impolite

Read the sentences. Find the words with the prefixes *im-* and *in-* and the words with the endings *-ed* and *-ing*. Write the words in the chart.

1. My homework was incomplete.
2. Tony was inactive for a while.
3. Walking on the water was impossible.
4. He waited for his friend.
5. He was impolite.

im-	*in-*
-ed	**-ing**

© Cengage Learning, Inc.

"Quicksand: When Earth Turns to Liquid"

Use this passage to practice reading with proper intonation.

What Is Quicksand?

The word *quicksand* makes some people shiver with fear.	9
This is probably because of the way many movies show	19
quicksand. In films, quicksand is often a mysterious substance	28
that sucks people and animals to their deaths!	36
Actual quicksand is very different from movie quicksand.	44
It rarely harms people or animals. Real quicksand is not	54
mysterious. It is a simple substance that forms naturally.	63

From "Quicksand: When Earth Turns to Liquid," pages 48 and 49

Intonation

B ☐ Does not change pitch.   A ☐ Changes pitch to match some of the content.

I ☐ Changes pitch, but does not match content.   AH ☐ Changes pitch to match all of the content.

Accuracy and Rate Formula

Use the formula to measure a reader's accuracy and rate while reading aloud.

$$\underline{\hspace{3cm}} - \underline{\hspace{3cm}} = \underline{\hspace{3cm}}$$

words attempted   number of errors   words correct per minute
in one minute   (wcpm)

Cengage Learning, Inc.

Name _____   Date _____

"Meet Maycira Costa"

Complete the double-entry log as you read "Meet Maycira Costa."

What I read	What it means to me
Page _____	_____
_____	_____
_____	_____
_____	_____
_____	_____
Page _____	_____
_____	_____
_____	_____
_____	_____
_____	_____
Page _____	_____
_____	_____
_____	_____
_____	_____
_____	_____

Tell a partner which part of the selection you found most interesting and why.

© Cengage Learning, Inc.

Name _____ Date _____

Compare Text Features

Use the Venn diagram to compare a science article and an interview.

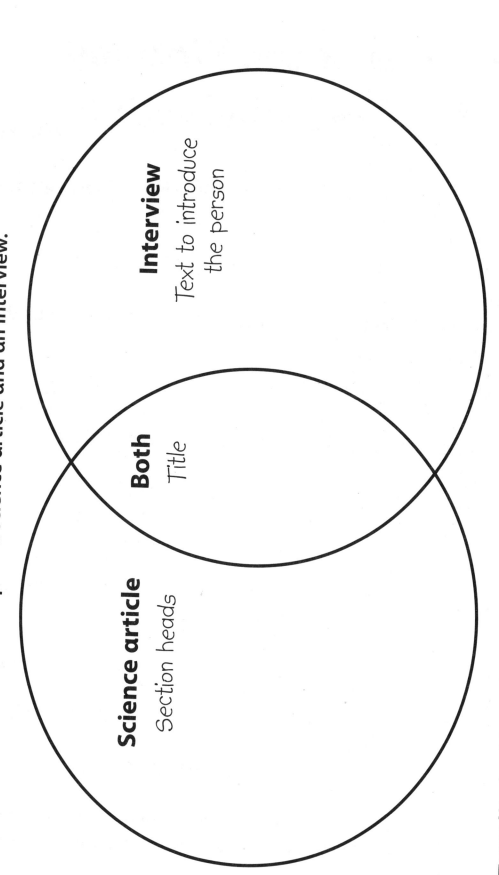

Science article
Section heads

Both
Title

Interview
Text to introduce the person

Work with a partner. Take turns interviewing each other about the science article and the interview. What text features did you like? What text features did your partner like?

5.20

Writing Project

Edit and Proofread

Use revision marks to edit and
proofread this paragraph. Look for:

- correct spelling with *-ed* and *-ing*
- correct use of apostrophes with
  possessive nouns
- correct possessive adjectives

Revision Marks	
∧	Add
℈	Take out
⌄̓	Add apostrophe

I thought that "Melt the Snow!" was a very funny play. I laughed

when I read that a snowflake was traping Hormiguitas leg. It was

funny to think that Cloud, Wind, and Wall were all stoping Sun

from shining, but little Mouses chewing helped them all. "Melt the

Snow!" is one of her favorite stories. I hope my sister reads it in their

class, too.

© Cengage Learning, Inc.

Name _____ Date _____

From Past to Present

Make a concept map with the answers to the Big Question:
How can we preserve our traditions?

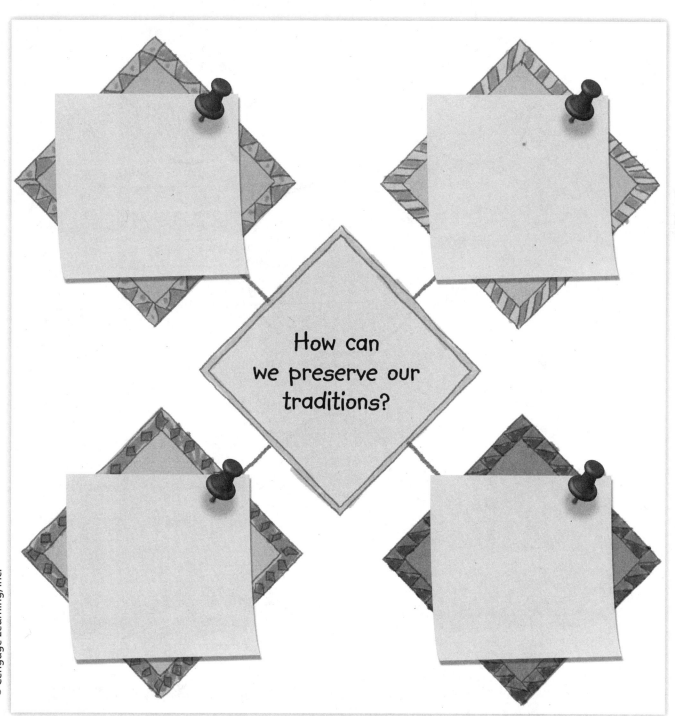

© Cengage Learning, Inc.

Thinking Map

"At the Festival"

Make a details web about things you find at a fair.

Use the details web to describe what you see, hear, smell, and taste at a fair to a partner.

© Cengage Learning, Inc.

Grammar

Fun at the Fair

Grammar Rules Subject Pronouns

A pronoun takes the place of a noun. A **subject pronoun** is the subject of the sentence.

Subject Pronouns	
Use for one	**Use for more than one**
I	we
you	you
he, she, it	they

Fill in the blanks with subject pronouns.

Dear Carmela,

    Last Saturday, my family went to the fair. _____ all had a great time. My sister loves rides. _____ rode the roller coaster. _____ looked too scary for me. I played games instead. My father loves salsa music. _____ danced with my mother. _____ were very good! What did I do? _____ ate a taco. _____ was delicious! _____ should come with us next time!

Your friend,
Alma

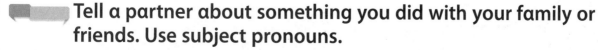 **Tell a partner about something you did with your family or friends. Use subject pronouns.**

© Cengage Learning, Inc.

Name _____   Date _____

"Shakira, Shakira!"

Listen as your teacher reads. Follow with your finger.

①

A girl hears and feels many things as she listens to the music of Shakira. She hears the twang of the lute and the soaring hum of the mijwiz. The Spanish lyrics and Lebanese drums create a rhythm that make the girl feel as though she's at a Colombian street party.

②

Shakira's music makes the girl feel happy and bright. She dances with scarves the way Shakira does. The music inspires her to learn Spanish so that she can really understand the songs.

③

Twenty years later, the girl, now grown up, is still inspired by Shakira's music. She shares it with her two daughters. Shakira's music makes them happy, too.

© Cengage Learning, Inc.

Grammar

Winning with Pronouns

Grammar Rules Object Pronouns

Use **object pronouns** in the predicate of a sentence. The object pronouns are **me**, **you**, **him**, **her**, **it**, **us**, **you**, and **them**.

1. Play with a partner. Place your markers on **music**.
2. Toss a coin. Move one space for heads. Move two spaces for tails.
3. If you land on an object pronoun, use it in a sentence.

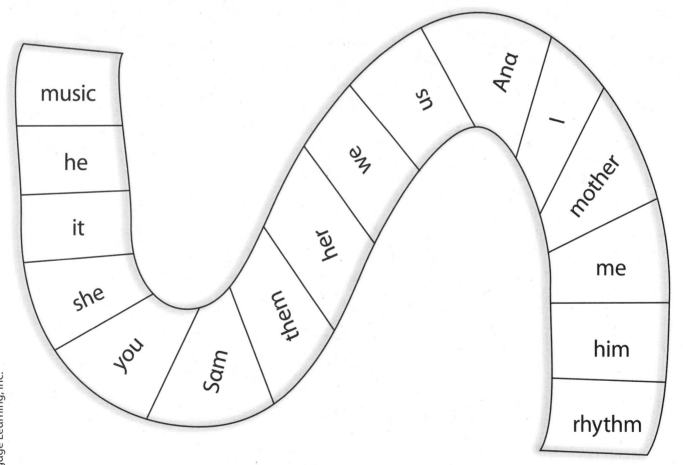

© Cengage Learning, Inc.

Tell a partner about something you saw or watched. Use object pronouns.

Name _____ Date _____

"Shakira, Shakira!"

Make a details web about Shakira's music.

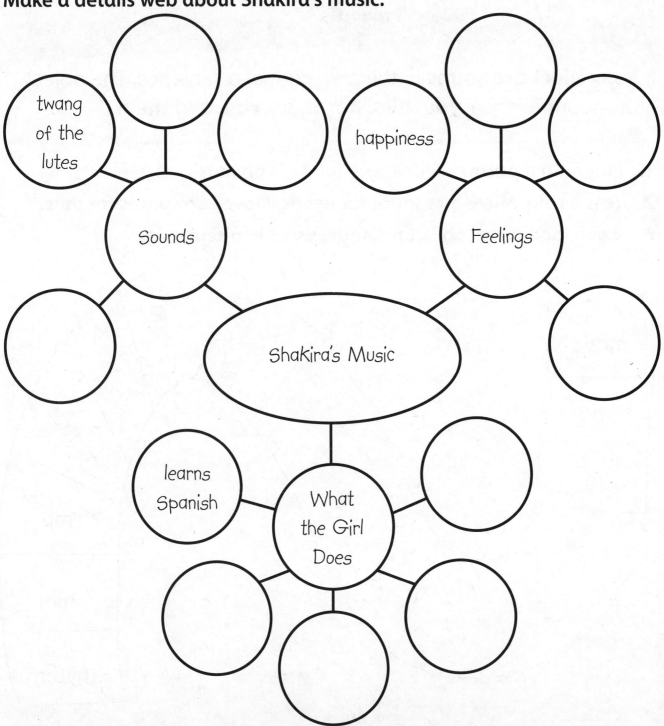

Use the details web to describe your favorite parts of the song lyrics to a partner.

© Cengage Learning, Inc.

Prefixes: re-, un-

retie   untied

Read each word. Circle the word that names the picture.

1.	reopen unmade unnamed	**2.**	repaint unknown unlock
3.	resend unsafe reset	**4.**	unsafe reread untied
5.	revert rewrite unpaid	**6.**	unhappy rewrapped revise

Read the sentences. Underline the words with prefixes.

I untied my laces and replaced them with new laces. Then I retied my shoes.

© Cengage Learning, Inc.

Fluency

"Shakira, Shakira!"

Use this passage to practice reading with proper expression.

In your songs, Shakira, I hear	6
the fusion of three regions.	11
So many sounds from each,	16
coming together	18
to make unforgettable music.	22
Bringing the musical heritage	26
of three different cultures	30
to the whole world.	34
And to me, on a foggy London day,	42
so many miles away,	46
Making me feel happy and bright,	52
despite the gloomy weather.	56

From "Shakira, Shakira!" page 93

Expression

B ☐ Does not read with feeling.

I ☐ Reads with some feeling, but does not match content.

A ☐ Reads with appropriate feeling for most content.

AH ☐ Reads with appropriate feeling for all content.

Accuracy and Rate Formula

Use the formula below to measure a reader's accuracy and rate while reading aloud.

$$\underset{\substack{\text{words attempted} \\ \text{in one minute}}}{\rule{3cm}{0.4pt}} - \underset{\substack{\text{number of errors}}}{\rule{3cm}{0.4pt}} = \underset{\substack{\text{words correct per minute} \\ \text{(wcpm)}}}{\rule{3cm}{0.4pt}}$$

© Cengage Learning, Inc.

Name _____ Date _____

"Blues Legend: Blind Lemon Jefferson"

Complete the journal as you read "Blues Legend: Blind Lemon Jefferson."

What I think	What my partner thinks
Page: _____ _____ _____ _____	_____ _____ _____ _____
Page: _____ _____ _____ _____	_____ _____ _____ _____
Page: _____ _____ _____ _____	_____ _____ _____ _____

Tell a partner what you thought about Blind Lemon Jefferson.

© Cengage Learning, Inc.

Name _____   Date _____

Compare Language

Use a T-chart to compare the language used in the lyrics to the language used in the biography.

Sensory language in the lyrics	Facts in the biography
1. The Spanish words, flowing and tumbling like a belly dancer's scarf.	**1.** Jefferson was born in Texas.
2.	**2.**
3.	**3.**
4.	**4.**

 Talk with a partner about the kind of language you hear in one of your favorite songs. Then compare that language with the language in the biography.

© Cengage Learning, Inc.

Grammar

My Musical Family

Grammar Rules Pronoun Agreement

	One	More than one
Use **subject pronouns** in the subject of a sentence.	I, you, he, she, it	we, you, they
Use **object pronouns** in the predicate of a sentence.	me, you, him, her, it	us, you, them

What pronouns can take the place of the underlined nouns? Write the correct **subject** or **object pronoun** on the line.

1. My brother and I like music. <u>My brother and I</u> play instruments. _____

2. I play the trumpet. I have played <u>the trumpet</u> since I was six years old. _____

3. My sister plays the guitar. <u>My sister</u> strums it and sings. _____

4. My father plays the piano. Many people ask <u>my father</u> for lessons. _____

5. My grandmother is a good singer. People often invite <u>my grandmother</u> to sing. _____

Tell a partner about people in your family and the music they like. Use the correct subject and object pronouns.

© Cengage Learning, Inc.

Thinking Map

Steps in a Process

Make a flow chart to show the steps of how to make something.

This is how to make a _____ .

Step 1:

↓

Step 2:

↓

Step 3:

↓

Step 4:

Use your flow chart to explain the steps to a partner.

© Cengage Learning, Inc.

Grammar

Near You or Far Away?

Grammar Rules Demonstrative Pronouns

A **demonstrative pronoun** points out things near you or far away.

Demonstrative Pronouns		
	One	More than one
Near you	this	these
Far away	that	those

Read the two sentences. Then write this, that, these, or those to complete the second sentence.

1. Here is a music book. Give _____ to Mr. Lopez.

2. The drums are across the room. Take _____ to the music room.

3. Get the poster boards from the closet. _____ will work best for your poster.

4. Here are some good markers. _____ are bright colors.

5. We will use the bulletin board in the hall. _____ will be a good place for the poster.

Draw yourself at the center of a picture. Draw things that are both near to you and far away. Then label the things this, that, these, or those.

© Cengage Learning, Inc.

Tell a partner how you labeled each object in your picture.

Key Points Reading

"Carving Stories in Cedar: How to Make a Totem Pole"

Listen as your teacher reads. Follow with your finger.

1

Hundreds of years ago, the first people who lived on the northwest coast of Canada and the United States wanted to tell stories about the past. They were not able to write their stories, so they made totem poles.

Israel Shotridge has carved totem poles for 20 years. Here are the steps he takes to make a totem pole:

2

a.

b.

c.

d.

e.

f.

a. He chooses a design.

b. He gets the tree ready. He draws the design on the wood.

c. He carves the pole with special tools.

d. The pole is painted in the traditional colors of red, teal, blue, and black.

e. When the totem pole is finished, everyone works together to raise it.

f. The pole is finished. It is time for a big party!

© Cengage Learning, Inc.

Grammar

Whose Project Is It?

Grammar Rules Possessive Pronouns

A **possessive pronoun** tells who or what owns something.

Possessive Pronouns	
One owner	**More than one owner**
mine	ours
yours	yours
his, hers, its	theirs

Choose the correct possessive pronoun.

1. Your class will visit _____ *ours* to see our projects.
   (ours/theirs)

2. Ben is still working on _____.
   (mine/his)

3. Lynn has finished _____. She made a clay pot.
   (hers/yours)

4. Maya made a quilt. "Can I see _____?" she asked me.
   (yours/ours)

5. "I just finished _____," I said. I held up my painting.
   (theirs/mine)

> Talk about something you have and something a partner has. Use two possessive pronouns.

© Cengage Learning, Inc.

Vocabulary

Vocabulary Bingo

Play Bingo using the Key Words from this unit.

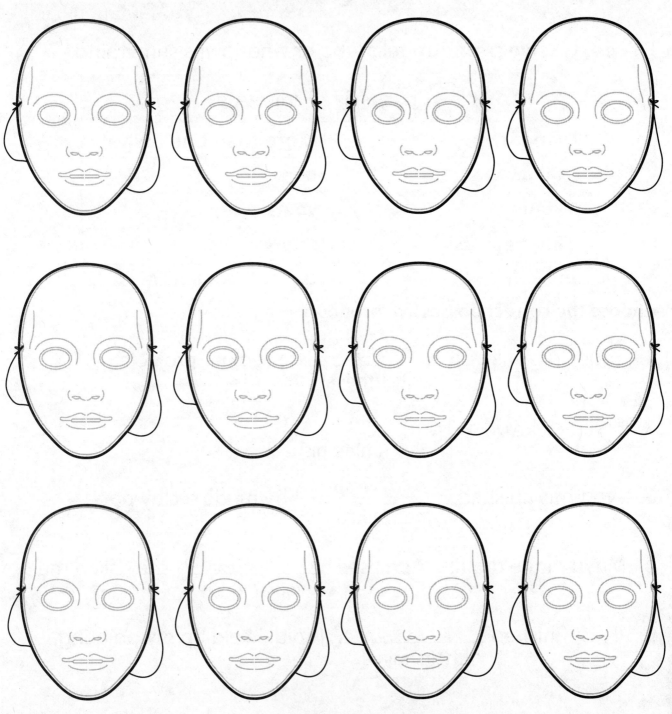

© Cengage Learning, Inc.

"Carving Stories in Cedar: How to Make a Totem Pole"

Make a flow chart of "Carving Stories in Cedar: How to Make a Totem Pole."

1. Shotridge chooses a design.

↓

2. He prepares the tree. He removes the bark and draws the design.

↓

3.

↓

4.

↓

5.

↓

6.

© Cengage Learning, Inc.

▶ **Use your flow chart to explain the steps to a partner.**

Phonics Practice

Prefixes: dis-, mis-

     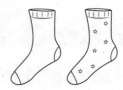

dislike   mismatch

Read each word. Circle the word that names the picture.

1.	disobey distance disconnect	**2.**	disagree dishonest dispose
3.	misstep mislay misfile	**4.**	mislead misuse misspell

Kat

Read the sentences. Underline the words with prefixes. Write the words with prefixes in the chart.

1. She was unhappy with her mistake.
2. Albert replaced the broken step.
3. It is bad to be dishonest.
4. Can you refill my glass?
5. I am disappointed because I misspelled a word.
6. The sidewalk was uneven.

dis-	*mis-*
re-	*un-*

© Cengage Learning, Inc.

© Cengage Learning, Inc.

Fluency

"The Legend of Raven and Fog Woman"

Use this passage to practice reading with proper intonation.

Raven asked, "How did you do that?"	7
Fog Woman didn't answer.	11
Day after day she filled the basket with water, and	21
soon the creek ran bright with salmon. No one in the	32
village went hungry.	35
But Raven wasn't satisfied. He clawed the ground with	44
his feet and flapped his wings angrily.	51
"Tell me your secret," Raven demanded.	57
Fog Woman wouldn't answer.	61
Raven lost his temper. "If you won't tell me, then go!"	72
he shouted.	74

From "The Legend of Raven and Fog Woman," pages 128 and 129

Intonation

B ☐ Does not change pitch.	A ☐ Changes pitch to match some of the content.
I ☐ Changes pitch, but does not match content.	AH ☐ Changes pitch to match all of the content.

Accuracy and Rate Formula

Use the formula below to measure a reader's intonation while reading aloud.

_____ − _____ = _____
Words attempted   number of errors   words correct per minute
  in one minute   (wcpm)

Name _____ Date _____

Read the Profile and Folk Tale

Complete one strategy planner for "Stories to Tell" and another for "The Rainbow Bridge."

Title:			
1. What is the author's purpose for writing?			
	to tell a story		to give information
	to entertain		
2. What is your purpose for reading?			
	for enjoyment		to get information
3. What type of selection are you going to read?			
	fiction		nonfiction
Do the following: • Identify the characters and setting. • Think about what happens and when it happens.		**Do the following:** • Read more slowly. • Identify facts about real people or events. • Use text features to find more information.	

 How did the strategies help you understand the selections?
Tell a partner which strategy was most helpful to you.

© Cengage Learning, Inc.

Respond and Extend

Compare Themes

Complete the theme webs to compare the legend and the folk tale.

Title: "The Legend of Raven and Fog Woman"

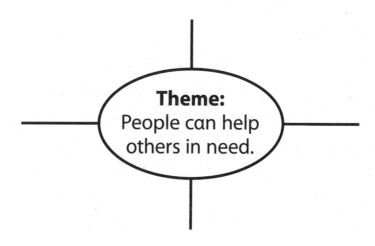

Theme:
People can help others in need.

Title: "The Rainbow Bridge"

Theme:
All kinds of people can live together in peace.

© Cengage Learning, Inc.

Take turns with a partner. Use the theme webs to talk about how the themes of the two tales are alike and how they are different.

Grammar

The Possessive Pronoun Game

Grammar Rules Pronoun Agreement

Possessive pronouns tell who or what owns something. Be sure to use the right possessive pronoun.

- For yourself, use **mine**.
- For yourself and one or more people, use **ours**.
- When you speak to one or more people, use **yours**.
- For one other person or thing, use **his**, **hers**, or **its**.
- For two or more people or things, use **theirs**.

1. **Play with a partner.**
2. **Spin the spinner.**
3. **Say a sentence using the possessive pronoun.**

Make a Spinner

1. Place one loop of a paper clip over the center of the circle.

2. Push a sharp pencil through the loop and the paper.

3. Spin the paper clip around the pencil.

© Cengage Learning, Inc.

Writing Project

Organization

Writing is organized when it is easy to follow. All the ideas make sense together and flow from one idea to the next in an order that fits the writer's audience and purpose.

	Is the writing organized? Does it fit the audience and purpose?	Does the writing flow?
4 Wow!	❑ The writing is very well-organized. It clearly fits both the writer's audience and purpose.	❑ The writing is smooth and logical. Each sentence flows into the next one.
3 Ahh.	❑ Most of the writing is organized. It mostly fits the writer's audience and purpose.	❑ Most of the writing is smooth. There are only a few sentences that do not flow logically.
2 Hmm.	❑ The writing is not well-organized. It fits the writer's audience or the writer's purpose, but not both.	❑ Some of the writing is smooth. Many sentences do not flow smoothly.
1 Huh?	❑ The writing is not organized at all. It does not fit the writer's audience or purpose.	❑ The sentences do not flow smoothly or logically.

© Cengage Learning, Inc.

Name _____   Date _____

Writing Project

Details Web

Complete the details web for your interview.

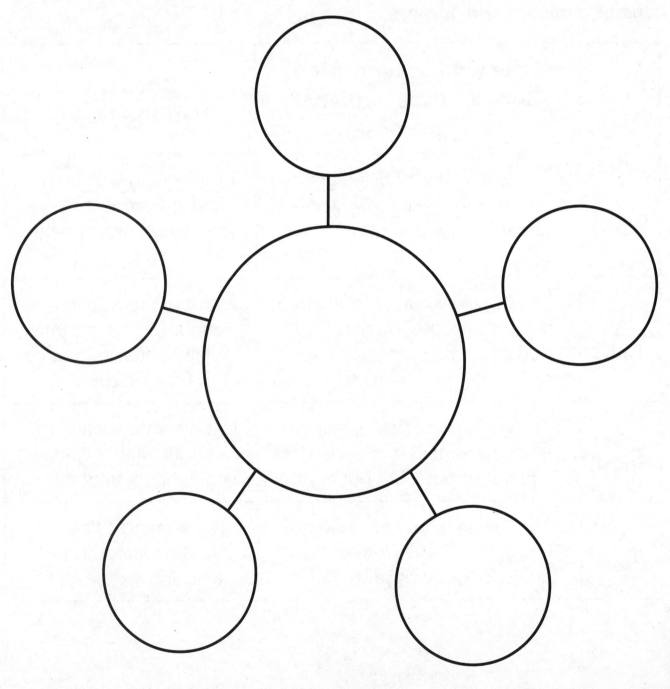

© Cengage Learning, Inc.

Writing Project

Revise

Use revision marks to make changes to this interview. Look for:

- **precise words**
- **strong beginning and ending**
- **logical order of questions**

Revision Marks	
^	Add
ℐ	Take out
⌒⌐	Move to here

Patchwork quilts are a special tradition of the American people. Many of them look nice.

Nadia: Why do you think it's important to preserve this tradition?

Aunt Paula: Because it's a reminder of the pioneers who settled parts of America a long time ago. It's a part of our history.

Nadia: What are patchwork quilts?

Aunt Paula: Patchwork is a type of quilt made with small pieces of fabric. Pioneer women had to make do with what they had, so they used small scraps of clothing and fabric to patch together a quilt.

© Cengage Learning, Inc.

Writing Project

Edit and Proofread

Use revision marks to edit and
proofread this paragraph. Look for:

- pronouns
- correct spelling of homophones
- capitalization of names and
  holidays

Revision Marks	
∧	Add
ﻉ	Take out
⌒⌒	Move to here
⌒SP	Check spelling
≡	Capitalize

Me interviewed my cousin maria about how to make a piñata

four birthday celebrations, christmas, and other holidays. Her makes

beautiful paintings on boxes. Then, she fills them with candies. She

wraps them in colorful foil paper and hangs them from a tree or a

place on the wall. They are saw pretty. my brothers and me don't

want to knock them down at first to get the candy! But, then we

finally do!

© Cengage Learning, Inc.

Name _____ Date _____

Blast! Crash! Splash!

Make a concept map with the answers to the Big Question:
What forces can change Earth?

What forces can change Earth?

volcano

© Cengage Learning, Inc.

Name _____   Date _____

Title: _____

Make an imagery chart about a story you know.

Place	Person	Thing

▸ **Use the imagery from your chart to tell the story to a partner.**

© Cengage Learning, Inc.

Name ______________________ Date ____________

Grammar

The Storm

Grammar Rules Adverbs

An **adverb** describes a verb. It tells **where**, **when**, or **how**.

Where	When	How
*I looked **down**.*	*It is raining **now**.*	*I ran **quickly**.*

Circle each adverb. Decide if it tells where, when, or how. Write each adverb in the correct place in the chart.

The wind blew hard yesterday. I looked up. Dark clouds rushed above. Rain started to fall lightly. Then, I heard a crash of thunder. The rain poured everywhere! I ran fast. I got to my house soon.

where	when	how
________	________	________
________	________	________
________	________	________

© Cengage Learning, Inc.

Use adverbs to tell a partner about a storm you saw.

Name _____ Date _____

"An Island Grows"

Listen as your teacher reads. Follow with your finger.

1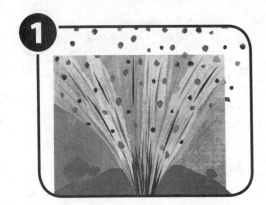

Deep under the ocean, rocks break apart. Water moves. A volcano blows lava into the water. Rocks come up from the ocean. The waves hit the rocks and sand piles up. An island is growing in the ocean. Trees and plants grow on the new island. Birds come to the island to live.

2

People see the island. Sailors use maps to find it. Settlers stay on the island. They build houses and use the soil to grow food. They have markets where people can buy and sell fish, fruit, and vegetables.

3

The island is busy with people and animals. But one day, near the island, the water moves. A volcano blows lava into the water. Another island grows.

© Cengage Learning, Inc.

Grammar

Build a Story

Grammar Rules Adverbs

To compare two actions, add **-er** to an **adverb**, or use the words **more** or **less** before the adverb.

Examples: *fast**er**, **more** quickly, **less** quickly*

To compare three or more actions, add **-est** to the adverb, or use the words **most** or **least** before the adverb.

Examples: *fast**est**, **most** quickly, **least** quickly*

1. Play "Tell a Tale Together" with a partner.

2. Take turns adding a sentence to build a story. Choose one or more words from the chart to score points.

3. Add up the points. The player with the most points is the winner.

1 point each	2 points each	2 points each
erupt	more	quickly
flow	the most	loudly
create	less	slowly
develop	the least	faster
		fastest
		sooner

 Use adverbs to tell a partner another tale.

© Cengage Learning, Inc.

"An Island Grows"

Make an imagery chart of "An Island Grows."

Volcano	Land	Plants	Animals	People
Stone breaks. Water quakes.				

💬 **Use your imagery chart to talk with a partner about your favorite parts of the poem.**

© Cengage Learning, Inc.

Phonics Practice

Suffixes: -ous, -sion, -tion

joy<u>ous</u>

colli<u>sion</u>

erup<u>tion</u>

Read each word. Circle the word that names the picture. Then write the word to complete each sentence.

1. $4 \div 2 = 2$ celebration division direction Do you think _____ is hard?	**2.**  vision nervous vacation We had fun on _____.
3.  education famous dangerous He is a _____ movie star!	**4.**  explosion explanation attention The _____ hurt my ears.

Read the sentences. Underline the words with suffixes.

On our vacation, we went in the wrong direction. We saw a dangerous bridge.

© Cengage Learning, Inc.

Fluency

"An Island Grows"

Use this passage to practice reading with proper intonation.

Markets sell.   2

Merchants yell.   4

"Fresh fish!"   6

"Pepper dish!"   8

"Ripe fruit!"   10

"Spicy root!"   12

From "An Island Grows," page 166

Intonation

B ☐ Does not change pitch.   A ☐ Changes pitch to match some of the content.

I ☐ Changes pitch, but does not match content.   AH ☐ Changes pitch to match all of the content.

Accuracy and Rate Formula

Use the formula to measure a reader's accuracy and rate while reading aloud.

$$\underline{\hspace{3cm}} - \underline{\hspace{3cm}} = \underline{\hspace{3cm}}$$

| words attempted in one minute | number of errors | words correct per minute (wcpm) |

© Cengage Learning, Inc.

Name _____ Date _____

"Volcano Views"

Complete the reflection journal as you read "Volcano Views."

Page	My question	The answer

➤ **Tell a partner which answer or fact was most interesting and why.**

© Cengage Learning, Inc.

Respond and Extend

Compare Texts

Write details from each text in the comparison chart. Add an asterisk (*) to details that are similar in both texts.

"An Island Grows"	"Volcano Views"
Tells about volcanoes under the sea	Tells about a man who photographs volcanoes
Tells about magma and lava	Tells about magma and lava

 Use the comparison chart to tell a partner which text you liked better and why.

© Cengage Learning, Inc.

Grammar

Volcanoes Rock!

Grammar Rules Adverbs

Adverbs tell more about a verb.

Examples: *Islands grow **slowly**.* (tells how)

*Some lava flows **faster** than other lava.*
(compares two actions)

*Thick lava flows **the least quickly** of all.*
(compares three or more actions)

Underline the adverbs.

I am a scientist. I see volcanoes erupt. I saw one yesterday.
The ground rumbled loudly. Rocks soon flew out. The lava flowed
more quickly than any lava I have seen. It glowed brightly.

The lava flows more slowly today. Ash floats everywhere. It is an
amazing sight!

Use adverbs to write three sentences about forces of nature.
Read your sentences to a partner.

© Cengage Learning, Inc.

Thinking Map

Underwater Earthquakes

Make a cause-and-effect chart about underwater earthquakes.

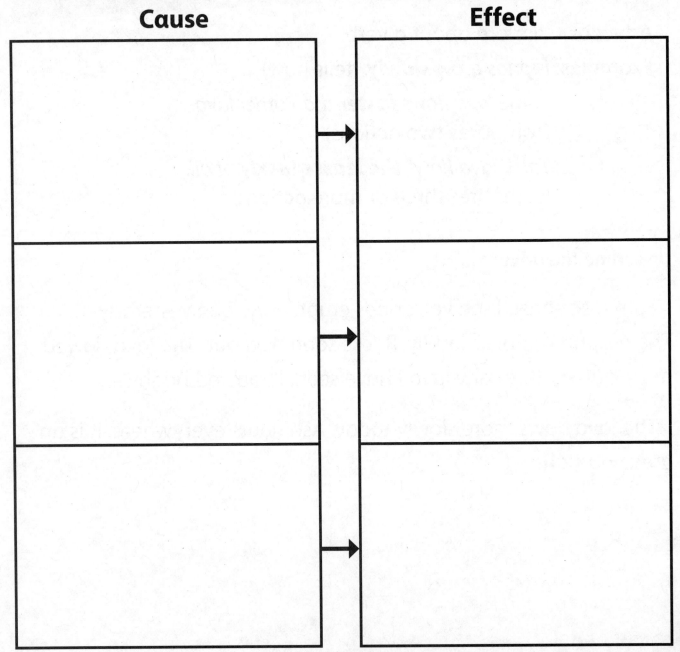

Cause   Effect

© Cengage Learning, Inc.

Use your chart to tell a partner about one cause-and-effect relationship related to a tsunami.

Grammar

On, Across, Before

Grammar Rules Prepositions

Some **prepositions** tell **where**, show **direction**, or show **time**.

Where	Direction	Time
on, near	into, from, across	before, during, after

Write a preposition from the chart to complete each sentence.

A tsunami is near, so we must drive away _____ the sea.

_____ the trip, Mom checks a map for the quickest way. Then

we all get _____ the car.

_____ our trip, Mom gives Dad directions. My sister sits

_____ me in the back. Soon, Dad drives _____ a bridge. We

see a town _____ the other side. _____ a short ride, we are

safe!

© Cengage Learning, Inc.

_____ **Use prepositions to tell a partner how you could get away from a storm.**

Name _____   Date _____

"Selvakumar Knew Better"

Listen as your teacher reads. Follow with your finger.

1
It was a beautiful day in December. Selvakumar's family was making breakfast, just like any other day. But Selvakumar knew something was wrong.

Selvakumar knew that big waves would soon come onto the shore. But his family did not. They needed to run to safety.

2
Papa saw the tsunami first. He told everyone to run. Mama took the two smallest boys and told Dinakaran to run up the hill. Dinakaran only heard her say, "Run!" and ran to the house instead.

But Selvakumar knew better. He made Dinakaran leave the house. They ran up the hill together. They were both safe.

3
After the tsunami ended, the family found each other on the hill. They hugged each other. They felt happy to be safe and alive.

They hugged Selvakumar, too, because he knew better. He saved Dinakaran's life!

© Cengage Learning, Inc.

Grammar

Before an Earthquake

Grammar Rules Prepositional Phrases

A preposition often has a noun or pronoun after it. Together, these words make a **prepositional phrase**.

Examples: *I went **to the store**.*

*I got a letter **from her**.*

Draw a line under the prepositional phrase in each sentence.

1. Karim lives near the shore.

2. One day, he feels the ground shake under his feet.

3. He runs into the house and tells his mother.

4. "We must leave before the tsunami," his mother says.

5. She packs food in the kitchen.

6. She loads a backpack and puts it on Karim's back.

7. They hurry from the town.

8. They go to a safe place.

9. They stay safe during the tsunami.

10. After the tsunami, they return home.

Decide with a partner whether each prepositional phrase tells where, shows direction, or shows time.

© Cengage Learning, Inc.

Reread and Retell

"Selvakumar Knew Better"

Make a cause-and-effect chart for "Selvakumar Knew Better."

Cause	Effect
Selvakumar hears a sound.	He whines and barks to warn his family.
Papa shouts, "Tsunami! Run!"	

🗨 **Use your chart to tell a partner about one cause-and-effect relationship you wrote about.**

© Cengage Learning, Inc.

Phonics Practice

Syllable Pattern: Consonant + -al, -el, -le

hospi<u>al</u>   la<u>bel</u>   mar<u>ble</u>

Read each word. Circle the word that names the picture. Then write the word to complete each sentence.

1. camel petal circle Stand in a _____ to play the game.	**2.** puzzle jungle angel The _____ has 1,000 pieces.
3. label petal metal You can see every _____ on this flower.	**4.** medal global jungle The winner gets a gold _____.

Read the sentences. Write the words with a consonant + -al, -el, -le and the words with suffixes -ous, -sion, -tion in the chart.

1. The jungle can be dangerous.
2. Read the label on the lotion.
3. The explosion bent the metal.

-al	-el	-le
-ous	**-sion**	**-tion**

© Cengage Learning, Inc.

Name _____ Date _____

"Selvakumar Knew Better"

Use this passage to practice reading with proper expression.

As Dinakaran and Selvakumar rested, they heard the	8
grownups talking.	10
"We'll never recover," moaned one man.	16
"We've lost absolutely everything," someone else said.	23
But Selvakumar felt the regular rhythm of Dinakaran's	31
chest rising and falling under his chin. Then he heard	41
Dinakaran's little brothers nearby. He smelled the familiar	49
scents of Papa and Mama.	54
And Selvakumar knew better.	58

From "Selvakumar Knew Better," page 202

Expression

B	☐ Does not read with feeling.	A	☐ Reads with appropriate feeling for most content.
I	☐ Reads with some feeling, but does not match content.	AH	☐ Reads with appropriate feeling for all content.

Accuracy and Rate Formula

Use the formula to measure a reader's accuracy and rate while reading aloud.

$$\underline{\hspace{2cm}} - \underline{\hspace{2cm}} = \underline{\hspace{2cm}}$$

words attempted in one minute	number of errors	words correct per minute (wcpm)

© Cengage Learning, Inc.

Name _____   Date _____

"Tsunami"

Complete the K-W-L-Q chart as you read "Tsunami."

K What I know	W What I want to know	L What I learned	Q Questions I still have

💬 Use your chart to tell two other classmates what you learned about tsunamis.

© Cengage Learning, Inc.

Respond and Extend

Compare Texts

Use a Venn diagram to compare "Selvakumar Knew Better" and "Tsunami."

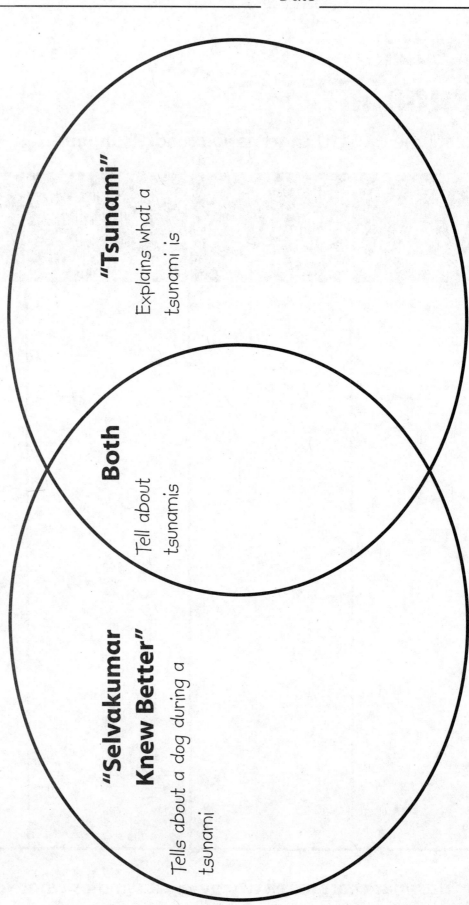

"Selvakumar Knew Better"

Tells about a dog during a tsunami

Both

Tell about tsunamis

"Tsunami"

Explains what a tsunami is

➤ **Tell a partner which text you liked better and why.**

© Cengage Learning, Inc.

Grammar

Preposition Tic-Tac-Toe

Grammar Rules Prepositional Phrases

Prepositional phrases:

- tell **where**
- show **direction**
- show **time**
- add **details**

Examples: *Jean's purse is **under the seat**.*
*The man walked **into the store**.*
*My cat sleeps **during the day**.*
Greg added some pepper
***to the stew**.*

1. Write one preposition in each box: **into, on, before, after, to, across, over, under, during.**

2. Your teacher will say a sentence with a prepositional phrase. Listen for the preposition in the sentence.

3. Put an "X" in the box with that preposition.

4. Once you have an "X" in a complete row or column, yell, "Three in a row! Tic-Tac-Toe!"

 Point to a preposition in your chart and ask a partner to use it in a sentence. Say another sentence that uses the preposition.

© Cengage Learning, Inc.

Name _____ Date _____

Organization

Writing is organized when it is easy to follow. All the ideas make sense together and flow from one idea to the next in an order that fits the writer's audience and purpose.

	Is the writing organized? Does it fit the audience and purpose?	Does the writing flow?
4 Wow!	❑ The writing is very well-organized. ❑ It clearly fits both the writer's audience and purpose.	❑ The writing is smooth and logical. Each sentence flows into the next one.
3 Ahh.	❑ Most of the writing is organized. ❑ It mostly fits the writer's audience and purpose.	❑ Most of the writing is smooth. There are only a few sentences that do not flow logically.
2 Hmm.	❑ The writing is not well-organized. ❑ It fits the writer's audience or the writer's purpose, but not both.	❑ Some of the writing is smooth. Many sentences do not flow smoothly.
1 Huh?	❑ The writing is not organized at all. ❑ It does not fit the writer's audience or purpose.	❑ The sentences do not flow smoothly or logically.

© Cengage Learning, Inc.

© Cengage Learning, Inc.

Writing Project

Main Idea and Details Diagram

Complete a main idea and details diagram for each paragraph of your research report.

Main idea:

Detail:

Detail:

Detail:

Detail:

Detail:

Writing Project

Revise

Use revision marks to make changes to this paragraph. Look for:

- information that has been paraphrased, not plagiarized
- smooth flow of ideas

Revision Marks	
∧	Add
ᵧ	Take out
⬭⟍	Move to here

Tsunamis are a series of destructive sea waves caused by an earthquake or volcanic eruption. What are tsunamis? When the waves reach land, they can be 100 feet high and cause a lot of destruction. Tsunamis are a frequent occurrence in Japan.

© Cengage Learning, Inc.

Writing Project

Edit and Proofread

Use revision marks to edit and proofread this paragraph. Look for:

- adverbs
- prepositions
- commas in a series
- spelling of compound words

Revision Marks	
∧	Add
℘	Take out
⬭⌐	Move to here
⬭ SP	Check spelling
ˌ	Add comma

Earth is made up of layers. A crack underneath the crust causes

a fault, or thin line of rock crushed between two blocks of rock.

The fault can be vertical horizontal or at an angle. When the Earth

cracks sudden, the ground can start to shake. The Earth shakes

furious with the onset beside an eartquake.

© Cengage Learning, Inc.

Unit Concept Map

Getting There

Make a concept map with the answers to the Big Question:
What tools can we use to achieve our goals?

What tools can we use to achieve our goals?

© Cengage Learning, Inc.

© Cengage Learning, Inc.

Thinking Map

The Big Race

Make a story map about a goal and outcome in life.

Goal

Events

Outcome

Talk with a partner about how each event relates to the goal and the outcome.

Grammar

Fun Run

Grammar Rules Regular Past Tense Verbs

Use **past tense verbs** to tell about something that already happened.

1. For most verbs, add **-ed**.
   Example: *talk* → *talk**ed***

2. If a verb ends in silent **e**, drop the **e** and add **-ed**.
   Example: *live* → *liv**ed***

3. If a one-syllable verb ends in one vowel and one consonant, double the consonant and add **-ed**.
   Example: *tap* → *tap**ped***

Fill in the blanks with past tense verbs.

My friend _____ me to go to a "fun run" with her. I _____
            (ask)   (enjoy)
it, but I had one problem. When the race _____, I _____ over
                                          (start)   (trip)
my shoelace and fell down! My friend _____ me up. Other
                                      (help)
runners _____ to see if I was okay. I _____ up and kept
         (stop)   (jump)
running. The rest of the race was fun. The runners _____ and
                                                    (laugh)
_____ during the race. When it _____, we _____ delicious
(chat)   (end)   (share)
cookies. Yum! It was truly a fun run!

▬▬ **Tell a partner about something you did last weekend.
Use past tense verbs.**

© Cengage Learning, Inc.

© Cengage Learning, Inc.

Key Points Reading

"Running Shoes"

Listen as your teacher reads. Follow with your finger.

1 Every year, the number man comes. He counts everyone in Sophy's village. One year, he sees Sophy looking at his running shoes. She wants a pair like them. They can make her wish come true. In a month, Sophy receives a pair of running shoes in the mail.

2 Sophy asks her mother if she can go to school. Her mother says it is too far away. Sophy says that she has running shoes now. She can run there. Her mom smiles and tells her she can go. The next day, Sophy runs the whole way to school. She tells the teacher that she wants to learn to read and write. The boys laugh at her, but Sophy wins a race against them, and they all become friends.

3 One year later, the number man comes back to Sophy's village. She tells him that her dream is to help build a school in her village and to become a teacher.

Grammar

From Present to Past

Grammar Rules Irregular Past Tense Verbs

Some verbs change in special ways to show an action in the past:

Now	am/is	are	do/does	go/goes
Past	was	were	did	went

1. **Play with a partner.**

2. **Spin the spinner.**

3. **Change the present tense verb to the past tense. Spell the past tense form and use it in a sentence.**

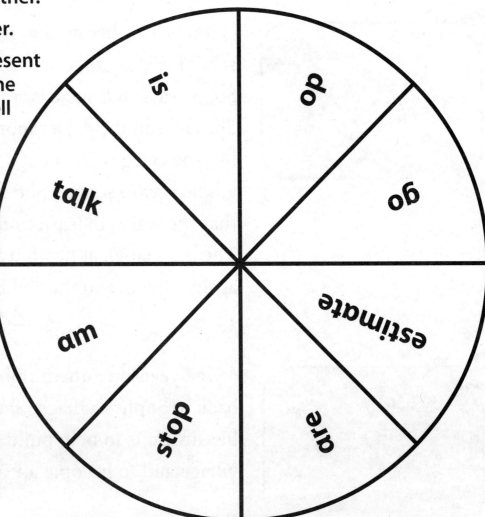

Make a Spinner

1. Place one loop of a paper clip over the center of the circle.

2. Push a sharp pencil through the loop and the paper.

3. Spin the paper clip around the pencil.

© Cengage Learning, Inc.

Name _____   Date _____

"Running Shoes"

Make a story map for "Running Shoes."

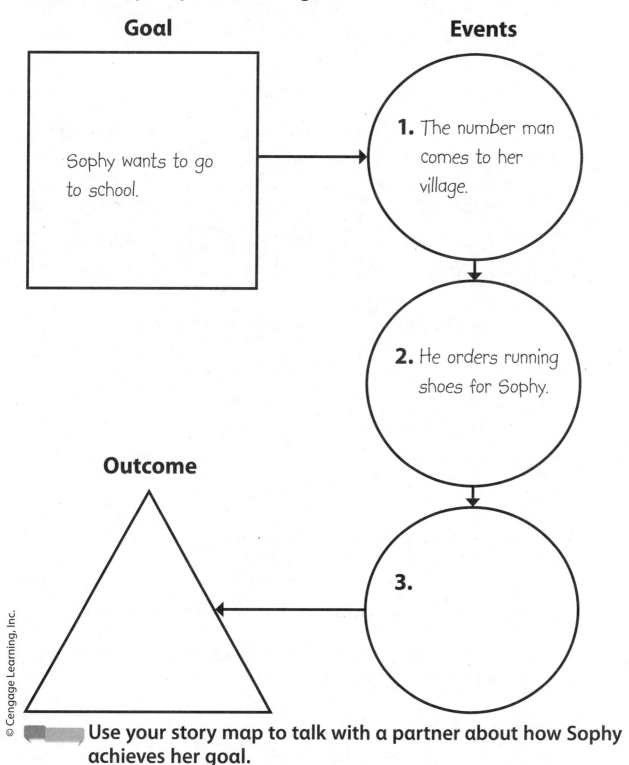

Goal

Sophy wants to go to school.

Events

1. The number man comes to her village.

2. He orders running shoes for Sophy.

3.

Outcome

▬▬ Use your story map to talk with a partner about how Sophy achieves her goal.

© Cengage Learning, Inc.

Phonics Practice

Suffixes: -ant, -ent

attend<u>ant</u>

pres<u>ent</u>

Read each word. Circle the word that names the picture. Then write the word to complete each sentence.

1.  distant pleasant student The _____ is learning to read.	**2.**  accident president different The cars were in an _____.
3.  student different immigrant They are not the same. They are _____.	**4.**  president distant servant She is the _____ of the company.

Read the sentences. Underline the words with the suffixes -ant or -ent.

An immigrant moves from one country to a different country. The new country may be a distant country.

© Cengage Learning, Inc.

© Cengage Learning, Inc.

Fluency

"Running Shoes"

Use this passage to practice reading with proper intonation.

"Running shoes!" she yelled. She carefully put   7

on each shoe. "Now my wish will come true."   16

"What wish?" her mother asked.   21

"I want to go to school."   27

"But the school is eight kilometers away over horrible roads."   37

"Yes, but now I have running shoes!" Sophy said as she   48

bounced up and down.   52

From "Running Shoes," page 238

Intonation

[B] ☐ Does not change pitch.   [A] ☐ Changes pitch to match some of the content.

[I] ☐ Changes pitch, but does not match content.   [AH] ☐ Changes pitch to match all of the content.

Accuracy and Rate Formula

Use the formula to measure a reader's accuracy and rate while reading aloud.

_____ − _____ = _____
words attempted   number of errors   words corrected per
in one minute   minute (wcpm)

Grammar

After School

> ## Grammar Rules Present and Past Tense Verbs
>
> Use **present tense verbs** to tell about an action that happens now or happens often.
>
> Use **past tense verbs** to tell about an action that already happened.
>
> Examples: **Present tense** → I **run** three kilometers every day.
>
> **Past tense** → I **ran** three kilometers yesterday.

Fill in the blanks with present tense or past tense verbs.

Every day after school, I _____ soccer. Yesterday, we _____
                              (play)   (play)
a game. At first, I _____ nothing. I _____ on the bench.
                     (do)   (am)
I _____ my friends. Then the coach _____ over to me.
  (watch)   (run)

"Maria," she said, "You always _____ fast. You always _____
                                 (run)   (kick)
the ball well. We _____ you now."
                    (need)

I _____ out on the field. I _____ a goal! Our team _____
  (go)   (score)   (is)
the winner!

© Cengage Learning, Inc.

Tell a partner about something you did yesterday and something you do almost every day. Use past tense and present tense verbs.

© Cengage Learning, Inc.

Thinking Map

A Traveler's Adventure

Make a main idea diagram with this main idea:
There are many interesting places to visit.

Main idea

There are many interesting places to visit.

Details

➜ Take turns with a partner adding other details that could support the main idea.

Grammar

I Will Explore the World

Grammar Rules Future Tense with *will*

To tell about an action in the **future**, you can use the helping verb **will** with the **main verb**.

Example: *Our class **will go** on a field trip next week.*

Fill in the blank with the future tense form of each underlined verb.

1. I often <u>visit</u> the children's museum.

    Next week, I _____ a new room there.

2. In this room, you can <u>learn</u> about places around the world.

    I _____ about new places to explore.

3. You can <u>use</u> math to figure out how far away each place is.

    I _____ math to figure out the distance to Hawaii.

4. People <u>fly</u> across the Pacific Ocean to Hawaii.

    Someday, I _____ there, too.

5. People <u>explore</u> Hawaii's beaches and volcanoes.

    I _____ all of its islands.

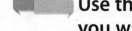 **Use three of the verbs above to tell a partner about something you will do in the future.**

© Cengage Learning, Inc.

Name _____   Date _____

"One Man's Goal"

Listen as your teacher reads. Follow with your finger.

Erden Eruç has a goal. He is going to row, bike, walk, and climb around the world using his own power. He is also going to climb the highest mountain on each of six continents.

Eruç made his trip in two parts. In the first part, Eruç biked 5,546 miles from Seattle, Washington, to Mt. McKinley, Alaska. Then he climbed 20,320 feet to the top of Mt. McKinley! In the second part, he rowed alone to Australia in a small boat.

Eruç knows that going around the world this way is a difficult goal. But he wants to show kids that they can do great things. Even though there may be hard parts, kids can reach their dreams and goals if they try.

© Cengage Learning, Inc.

Grammar

The Destination Game

Grammar Rules Future Tense with *am/is/are going to*

To tell about an action in the **future**, you can use **am going to**, **is going to**, or **are going to** before a main verb.

Examples: *I **am going to** travel.*

*Pedro **is going to** travel.*

*Pedro and Maria **are going to** travel.*

1. **Play with a partner.**

2. **Spin the spinner.**

3. **Use the word or words as the subject of a sentence. Tell where each subject is going to travel to or explore in the future.**

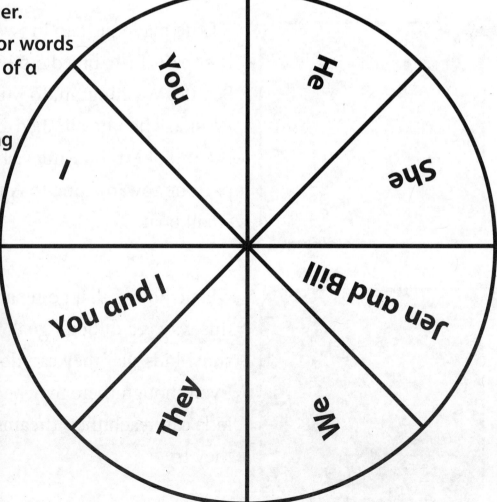

Make a Spinner

1. Place one loop of a paper clip over the center of the circle.

2. Push a sharp pencil through the loop and the paper.

3. Spin the paper clip around the pencil.

© Cengage Learning, Inc.

Reread and Retell

"One Man's Goal"

Make a main idea diagram for different sections of "One Man's Goal."

Main idea	Details
Eruç decided to travel around the world.	He left California in a boat in 2007.
	He rowed across the Pacific Ocean to Australia.

 Use your main idea diagram to summarize parts of the selection for a partner.

© Cengage Learning, Inc.

Phonics Practice

Words with More Than One Syllable

pa/per   re/cy/cle   al/li/ga/tor

Read each word. Clap the syllables. Color a hand for each clap.

1.   potato

2.   student

3.   immigrant

4.    information

Read the sentences. Underline the words with more than one syllable. Circle the words with the suffixes -*ant* or -*ent*. Write the words in the chart.

1. I saw a magnificent play.
2. The principal gave a pleasant speech.
3. The accident was bad.
4. He came from a distant land.

2 syllables	3 syllables	4 syllables
-ant	-ent	

© Cengage Learning, Inc.

Fluency

"One Man's Goal"

Use this passage to practice reading with proper phrasing.

Crossing the Pacific was amazing, but that was	8
only part of Eruç's journey. He was determined to	17
go around the world—using his own energy!	25
During his journey, Eruç wanted to climb the tallest	34
peaks on six continents to honor the memory of a	44
fellow climber. Eruç planned to bike, walk, climb, and	53
row the world—without any motors to help him.	62

From "One Man's Goal," page 273

Phrasing

B ☐ Rarely pauses while reading the text.   **A** ☐ Frequently pauses at appropriate points in the text.

I ☐ Occasionally pauses while reading the text.   **AH** ☐ Consistently pauses at all appropriate points in the text.

Accuracy and Rate Formula

Use the formula to measure a reader's accuracy and rate while reading aloud.

$$\underset{\substack{\text{words attempted} \\ \text{in one minute}}}{\underline{\hspace{3cm}}} - \underset{\substack{\text{number of errors}}}{\underline{\hspace{3cm}}} = \underset{\substack{\text{words corrected per} \\ \text{minute (wcpm)}}}{\underline{\hspace{3cm}}}$$

© Cengage Learning, Inc.

Name _____   Date _____

"Climbing Toward Her Goal"

Write about new words you learn as you read "Climbing Toward Her Goal."

 # Word Detective

New word: _____

What I think it means: _____

_____

 Clues: _____

_____

 Definition: _____

_____

- -

 # Word Detective

New word: _____

What I think it means: _____

_____

 Clues: _____

_____

 Definition: _____

_____

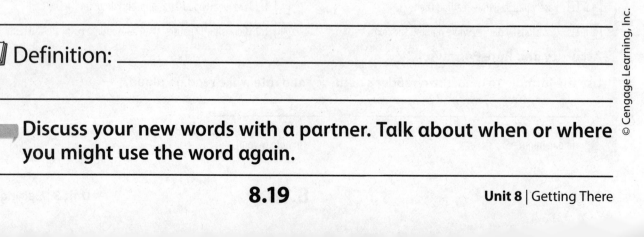 **Discuss your new words with a partner. Talk about when or where you might use the word again.**

© Cengage Learning, Inc.

© Cengage Learning, Inc.

Respond and Extend

Compare Causes

Use the Venn diagram to compare Erden Eruç and Constanza Ceruti.

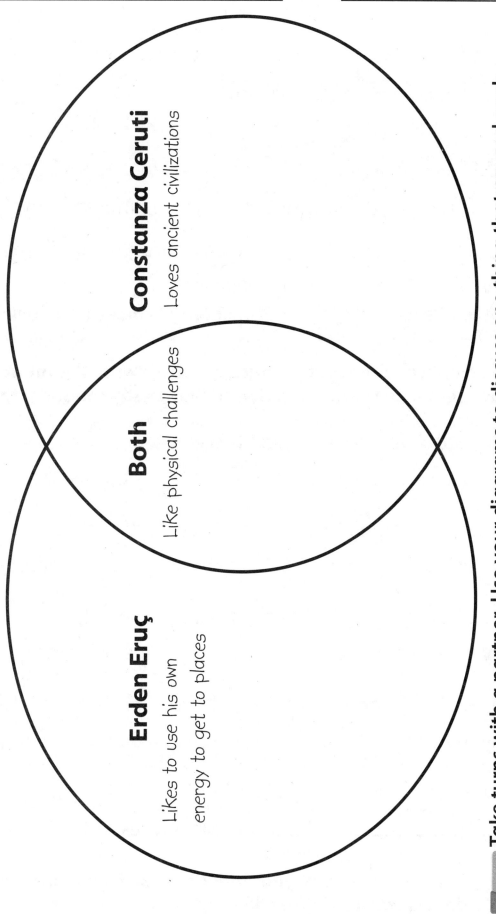

Erden Eruç

Likes to use his own energy to get to places

Both

Like physical challenges

Constanza Ceruti

Loves ancient civilizations

Take turns with a partner. Use your diagrams to discuss one thing that caused each person to begin an adventure.

Grammar

A Busy Weekend

Grammar Rules Future Tense

You can show the **future tense** in two different ways.

Use **will** + a **main verb**:	Use **am/is/are** + **going to** + a **main verb**:
Example:	Example:
I **will make** tacos tonight.	I **am going to make** tacos tonight.

Each sentence tells about a future action. Rewrite the future tense verb in each sentence to show a different way to say the same thing.

1. I will study for my math test this weekend.

I _____ for my math test this weekend.

2. My sister is going to practice her basketball skills.

My sister _____ her basketball skills.

3. My brothers will prepare their science project.

My brothers _____ their science project.

4. My mother is going to help Aunt Sally move to a new home.

My mother _____ Aunt Sally move to a new home.

5. It will be a very busy weekend.

It _____ a very busy weekend.

💬 **Tell a partner what your friends or family members will probably do this weekend. Use will or going to.**

© Cengage Learning, Inc.

Writing Project

Voice

Every writer has a special way of saying things, or a voice. The voice should sound genuine, or real, and be unique to that writer.

	Does the writing sound genuine and unique?	Does the tone fit the audience and purpose?
4 Wow!	❏ The writing is genuine and unique. It shows who the writer is.	❏ The writer's tone, formal or informal, fits the audience and purpose.
3 Ahh.	❏ Most of the writing sounds genuine and unique.	❏ The writer's tone mostly fits the audience and purpose.
2 Hmm.	❏ Some of the writing sounds genuine and unique.	❏ Some of the writing fits the audience and purpose.
1 Huh?	❏ The writing does not sound genuine or unique.	❏ The writer's tone does not fit the audience or purpose.

© Cengage Learning, Inc.

Writing Project

Story Map

Complete a story map for your story.

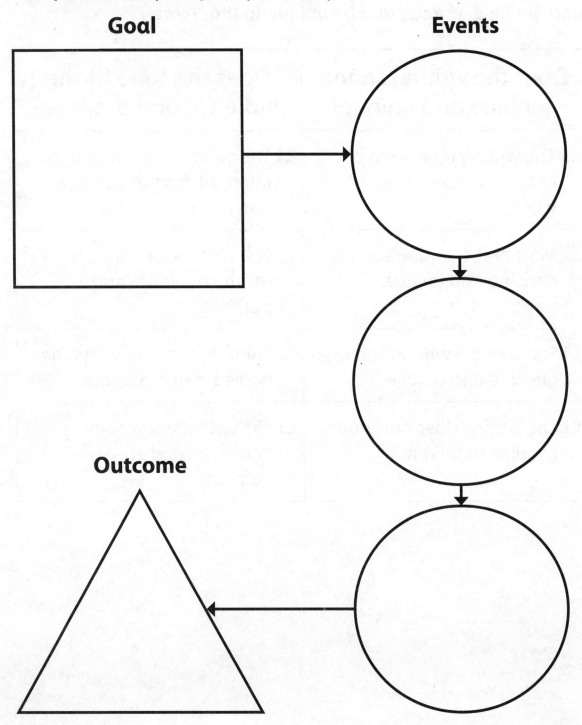

Goal

Events

Outcome

© Cengage Learning, Inc.

Writing Project

Revise

Use revision marks to make changes to these paragraphs. Look for:
- details that tell about setting
- words that show personal voice

Revision Marks	
∧	Add
ℱ	Take out

My friend Mina loves to roller skate. She roller skates every

Saturday at the rink. Almost nothing can keep her away.

Then about a month ago, she fell and hurt her ankle really badly.

She was laid up for several weeks. One day, I went to visit her.

I found her staring out a window. Without turning toward me, she

said, "I will be roller skating in a month." Knowing Mina, I didn't

doubt her. Still, she had hurt her ankle pretty badly.

Sure enough, a month later, she was there with her roller skates.

© Cengage Learning, Inc.

Writing Project

Edit and Proofread

Use revision marks to edit and
proofread this paragraph. Look for:

- verb tenses
- punctuation with dialogue

	Revision Marks	
∧	Add	
ℱ	Take out	
ᵛ ᵛ	Insert quotation marks	
ᵔ	Insert comma	
⌃	Insert period	
⌃	Insert question mark	
⌃	Insert exclamation point	

Sarah Nist the announcer called. The crowd stood up and

applauds wildly. Sarah glided onto the ice. Her left leg slided a bit

as she points her right leg straight out behind her into a graceful

arabesque. The crowd went wild again and screamed, Go Sarah Only

a year ago, she had struggled to walk after an accident. Now, she was

on her way to victory again.

© Cengage Learning, Inc.

Photographic Credits

5.14 (t) pio3/Shutterstock.com. (c) Jupiterimages/Getty Images. 6.14 (tl) Ed Reschke/Getty Images. (cl) gary warnimont/Alamy Stock Photo. (tr) Shotridge Studios. (bl) Shotridge Studios (cr) Melissa Farlow/National Geographic Image Collection. (cl) Shotridge Studios. (br) Danita Delimont/Getty Images. 7.1 (inset) Colin Anderson/Getty Images. 8.14 (t) ERDEN ERUC/United Press International (UPI)/Newscom. (b) Erden Eruc.

© Cengage Learning, Inc.